GRAMMAR, PUNCTUATION & SPELLING
BOOSTER

Workbook

Do not
write in this
book

Scholastic Education, an imprint of Scholastic Ltd

Book End, Range Road, Witney, Oxfordshire, OX29 0YD

Registered office: Westfield Road, Southam, Warwickshire CV47 0RA

www.scholastic.co.uk

© 2016, Scholastic Ltd

1 2 3 4 5 6 7 8 9   6 7 8 9 0 1 2 3 4 5

British Library Cataloguing-in-Publication Data

A catalogue record for this book is available from the British Library.

ISBN 978-1407-16083-2

Printed and bound by Ashford Colour Press

Extracts from National Curriculum for England, English Programme of Study © Crown Copyright. Reproduced under the terms of the Open Government Licence (OGL). www.nationalarchives.gov.uk/doc/open-government-licence/version/3/

Author Shelley Welsh

Editorial Rachel Morgan, Anna Hall, Sam Pope, Mary Nathan

Cover and Series Design Neil Salt and Nicolle Thomas

Layout Claire Green

Illustrations Dan Lewis @ Beehive Illustration

Contents

How to use this book

This book will help you with what you need to know before you take the National Tests. You can complete Practice Test A first and use the grid to focus on specific topics you need more help on, or you can work through all of the activities in this book.

You can check the answers at **www.scholastic.co.uk/boosteranswers.**

The title of the topic.

What you should be able to do after you complete this page. You can tick off each one as you can do it.

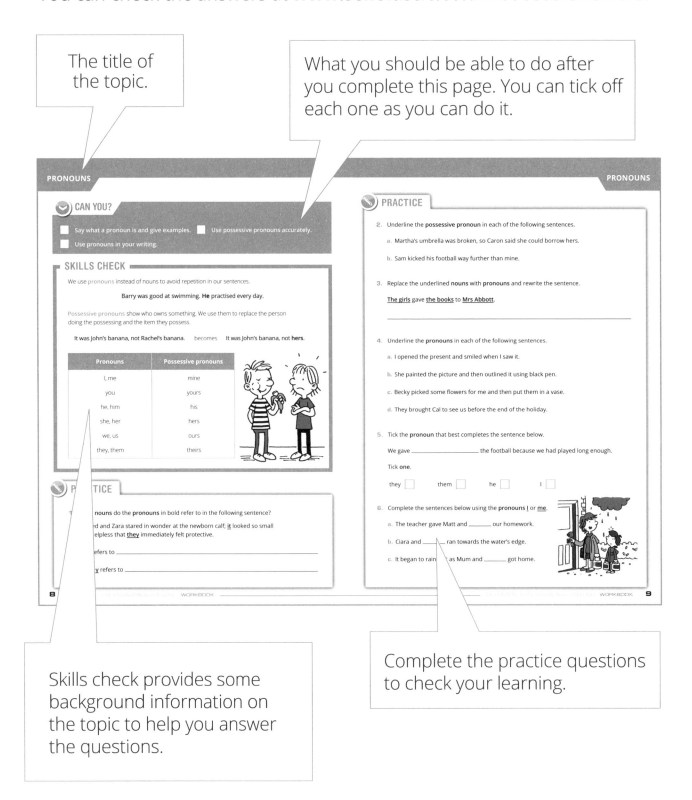

Skills check provides some background information on the topic to help you answer the questions.

Complete the practice questions to check your learning.

Progress chart

Topic	Revised	Practised	Achieved
Word classes			
Pronouns			
Determiners			
Prepositions			
Sentence types			
Conjunctions and relative clauses			
Expanded noun phrases			
Subjects, objects and subject-verb agreement			
Active and passive voice			
Verb tenses			
Modal verbs and adverbs			
Formal and informal speech and writing			
Capital letters and punctuation			
Brackets, dashes and commas to indicate parenthesis			
Semi-colons, colons and dashes			
Inverted commas			
Apostrophes to show contraction			
Apostrophes for possession			
Bullet points and ellipses			
Hyphens			
Synonyms and antonyms			
Word families			
Adding suffixes (1)			
Adding suffixes (2)			
Prefixes			
Homophones			
Silent letters			
The letter-string 'ough'			
Words with the /ee/ sound spelled 'ei' after 'c'			

 **CAN YOU?**

- [ ] Say what nouns and adjectives are.
- [ ] Explain the difference between an adjective and an adverb.
- [ ] Describe what a verb is.
- [ ] Say where a fronted adverbial comes in a sentence.

SKILLS CHECK

Nouns name people, places and things, and adjectives modify them.
There are two different types of nouns.

Common nouns	Proper nouns
• name general things • name groups of things like animals or people • name things that cannot be seen or touched, such as emotions • don't need a capital letter unless at the beginning of a sentence	• name specific things like people, places, days of the week • always need to start with a capital letter
book, pencil, phone, flower, sheep, family, tea, happiness, love, boredom	*Robert, Spain, Buckingham Palace*

Verbs are doing or being words. They are modified by adverbs. Adverbs often end in '**ly**'.

He ran through the house **quickly**.

An adverbial phrase is where more than one word is used to modify the verb.

I learned my tables **last night**.

Fronted adverbials are adverbs or adverbial phrases that come at the start of a sentence and are always followed by a comma.

The sentence below shows you the different word classes in a sentence.

Finally , the newborn baby slept peacefully through the night .

fronted adverbial | adjective | noun | verb | adverb | noun

 **PRACTICE**

1. **a.** Write a sentence using the word <u>hand</u> as a **noun**.

    _____

    b. Write a sentence using the word <u>hand</u> as a **verb**.

    _____

2. Complete the sentence with an **adjective** formed from the **verb** <u>apologise</u>.

    Our teacher was very _____ when she realised we had worked through our break.

3. Rewrite each sentence so that it includes a **fronted adverbial**. Remember to punctuate your sentences correctly.

    a. We went for a rest after our long journey.

    _____

    b. Grace swam in the sea cautiously.

    _____

4. Write the **word class** of each word or phrase in bold.

    > fronted adverbial   noun   adverb   adjective   verb

    a. We found some **<u>money</u>** on the footpath. _____

    b. The **<u>team</u>** practised their passing skills. _____

    c. Joe worked **<u>hard</u>** on his times tables. _____

    d. **<u>After a short break</u>**, Zak carried on writing. _____

    e. The children **<u>were being</u>** naughty. _____

    f. Mum mixed the **<u>ground</u>** spices into the curry. _____

    g. Summoning his **<u>courage</u>**, Jake faced the tiger. _____

CAN YOU?

- [ ] Say what a pronoun is and give examples.
- [ ] Use pronouns in your writing.
- [ ] Use possessive pronouns accurately.

SKILLS CHECK

We use pronouns instead of nouns to avoid repetition in our sentences.

Barry was good at swimming. He practised every day.

Possessive pronouns show who owns something. We use them to replace the person doing the possessing and the item they possess.

It was John's banana, not Rachel's banana.   becomes   It was John's banana, not **hers**.

Pronouns	Possessive pronouns
I, me	mine
you	yours
he, him	his
she, her	hers
we, us	ours
they, them	theirs

PRACTICE

1. What **nouns** do the **pronouns** in bold refer to in the following sentence?

   Ahmed and Zara stared in wonder at the newborn calf; **it** looked so small and helpless that **they** immediately felt protective.

   a. **it** refers to _____

   b. **they** refers to _____

PRACTICE

2. Underline the **possessive pronoun** in each of the following sentences.

   a. Martha's umbrella was broken, so Caron said she could borrow hers.

   b. Sam kicked his football way further than mine.

3. Replace the underlined **nouns** with **pronouns** and rewrite the sentence.

   The girls gave **the books** to **Mrs Abbott**.

   _____

4. Underline the **pronouns** in each of the following sentences.

   a. I opened the present and smiled when I saw it.

   b. She painted the picture and then outlined it using black pen.

   c. Becky picked some flowers for me and then put them in a vase.

   d. They brought Cal to see us before the end of the holiday.

5. Tick the **pronoun** that best completes the sentence below.

   We gave _____ the football because we had played long enough.

   Tick **one**.

   they ☐   them ☐   he ☐   I ☐

6. Complete the sentences below using the **pronouns** _I_ or _me_.

   a. The teacher gave Matt and _____ our homework.

   b. Ciara and _____ ran towards the water's edge.

   c. It began to rain just as Mum and _____ got home.

CAN YOU?

- [ ] Say what a determiner is.

- [ ] Explain when to use *an* instead of *a*.

- [ ] Give examples of determiners, including demonstrative and possessive determiners.

SKILLS CHECK

A determiner is a word that introduces a noun.
It goes before any modifiers, such as adjectives or other nouns.

a red apple

Articles are the most common types of determiner.
The article **the** is used to specify a 'known' noun.

The English teacher shut the door.

The article **a** is used to specify an 'unknown' noun.

A teacher came into the classroom.

If the article **a** comes before a word beginning with a vowel, it becomes **an**.

an orange, **an** opportunity

Possessive determiners (*my, his, her, your, its, our, their*) come before a noun and show that someone owns the noun. It replaces the possessor but not the item possessed.

It was not Rachel's banana.   becomes   It was not **her** banana.

Demonstrative determiners include *this, those* and *that*.

That boy won the race.

Determiners that show amounts include *some, every, all, none* and *lots of*.

Lots of people go to France on holiday.

PRACTICE

1. Circle all the **determiners** in the sentence below.

   After a late start, the runners finished the race in record time.

2. Write suitable **determiners** to complete the sentences below.

   At _____ zoo, we saw _____ monkeys, _____ elephant and _____ kangaroo.

3. Write the missing **demonstrative determiners** in the sentence below.

   _____ people prefer sweet food to savoury, whereas _____ people like both.

4. Circle the two **possessive determiners** in each sentence below.

   a. My new umbrella was a present for my eleventh birthday.

   b. Sam gave his brother a piece of toast for his breakfast.

   c. The boys kicked their football over my neighbour's fence.

   d. Our cousins like going to France for their holidays.

5. Which **pair of determiners** is missing from the sentence below?

   After _____ night of heavy rain, we were delighted to see _____ sun shining when we woke up.

   Tick **one**.

   the, a   ☐

   an, the   ☐

   a, the   ☐

6. Write the missing **possessive determiners** in the sentences below.

   a. Sinead's brother did _____ homework before he had _____ tea.

   b. Millie and Zac went to see _____ grandparents in _____ new home.

   c. I put _____ book on _____ bookshelf.

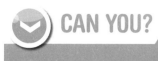

CAN YOU?

☐ Say where a preposition comes in a sentence.

☐ Use prepositions that indicate time.

☐ Give examples of prepositions of location.

☐ Include prepositions that show why something has happened.

SKILLS CHECK

A preposition is a word that normally comes before a noun or a pronoun. It tells us the relationship between two nearby words, for example:

where something is: *under, between, over, on, into*

the time when something happens: *on, at, after, since*

why something has happened: *because of, due to.*

Watch out for **because of**. The word *because* is only a preposition when it is followed by *of* and a noun. If *because* is followed by a clause, it is being used as a subordinating conjunction.

We were late **because of** the traffic jam.   We were late **because** we got caught in a traffic jam.

PRACTICE

1. Tick all the sentences that contain a **preposition**.

   Tanja's ball rolled under the table.   ☐

   We stayed inside because of the rain.   ☐

   Imran jumped into the swimming pool.   ☐

   Millie ate her breakfast and brushed her teeth.   ☐

2. Write an appropriate **preposition** to complete each sentence.

   a. I always go swimming _____ Saturday.

   b. We looked _____ the window at the dreadful weather.

   c. The fire alarm sounded _____ our history lesson.

   d. Samira found some money _____ the floor.

PRACTICE

3. Read the following passage and underline all the **prepositions**.

I went up to my bedroom and lay on my bed. Suddenly, I spotted an enormous spider in the corner of the ceiling! I put my hands over my eyes, and then peeped through my fingers. The spider had gone! Was it in my bed, under my pillow or, worst of all, on my head? I heard a knock at the door – phew! It was Mum. She came into my room and stood beside my bed. "What's this piece of black fluff on your cover?" she asked as she picked it up and threw it into the bin.

4. Read the passage below. Then tick the most suitable group of **prepositions** to complete it.

Brogan walked _____ the bridge, _____ the willow tree, _____ the winding path and before he knew it, he was standing _____ the entrance to the cave.

Tick **one.**

up	over	into	beside	☐
into	after	under	in	☐
under	across	beside	across	☐
over	around	along	before	☐

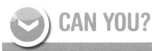 CAN YOU?

- ☐ Punctuate different sentence types.
- ☐ Use questions, commands and exclamations correctly.
- ☐ Explain what a statement is.
- ☐ Decide when to use a full stop or an exclamation mark.

SKILLS CHECK

A statement is a sentence that tells you something. It ends with a **full stop**.

June is a month of the year.

A question is a sentence that asks something. It ends with a **question mark**.

Is June a month of the year?

A command is a sentence that tells you to do something. It contains an imperative (bossy) verb, often at the beginning of the sentence, and ends either with a **full stop** or an **exclamation mark**.

Stop asking me if June is a month of the year!

An exclamation is a sentence where surprise, shock, pain or a strong emotion is expressed. It ends in an **exclamation mark**. It must be introduced with *how* or *what*, and it must contain a subject and a verb.

What terrible weather it is!

PRACTICE

1. Complete these **command sentences** using suitable **imperative verbs**.

    a. _____ your bedroom now, please!

    b. When you have finished your work, _____ it to your teacher.

    c. _____ your teeth quickly or we will be late for the bus.

    d. "Please _____ Mum with the washing up," said Dad.

2. Underline the words in the sentence below that make it a **question**.

    "You've asked Dad if he will take us swimming, haven't you?"

PRACTICE

3. Which final punctuation mark is missing from the sentence below?

Tick **one**.

How lovely it is to see you

question mark ☐   exclamation mark ☐   full stop ☐

4. Write a **question** that would match this answer.

I went to Spain for two weeks.

_____

5. Write an example of each of the following sentence types.

Sentence type	Sentence
a. exclamation	
b. question	
c. command	
d. statement	

6. The final punctuation is missing from each of these sentences. Tick one box in each row to indicate what sentence type each is.

Sentence	Statement	Command	Exclamation	Question
Insects have six legs				
Ask your brother to tidy his bedroom				
You've seen this film, haven't you				
What great big teeth that dog has				

7. Which two sentences below are punctuated correctly?

Tick **two**.

There were lots of people at the school fair. ☐

Were there lots of people at the school fair. ☐

Invite lots of people to the school fair! ☐

What a lot of people were at the school fair? ☐

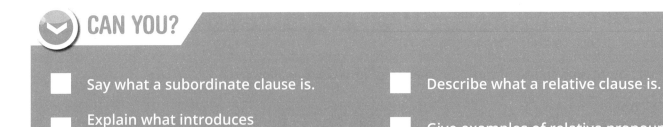

CAN YOU?

- [ ] Say what a subordinate clause is.
- [ ] Explain what introduces a subordinate clause.
- [ ] Describe what a relative clause is.
- [ ] Give examples of relative pronouns.

SKILLS CHECK

A subordinate clause is introduced by a subordinating conjunction like the ones listed below.

| however | because | although | unless | while |

A subordinate clause does not make sense on its own and is not a complete sentence. For example:

We didn't go outside today because it was too hot.

A co-ordinating conjunction links two words, phrases or clauses of equal importance.

| and | but | or | so | for | yet | nor |

Joy liked dancing **and** she went every Saturday to a class.

A relative clause is normally introduced by a relative pronoun.

| who | that | which | where | when | whose |

Relative clauses are used to define the noun that comes before them.
A relative clause is a type of subordinate clause.

The clown, who wore scary make-up, scared the children.

While subordinate clauses do not make sense on their own, main clauses do.

PRACTICE

1. Insert a suitable **relative pronoun** in the sentence below.

   The old man next door, _____ dog had been missing for hours, was delighted

   when we found it in our garden.

2. Continue the sentence by adding a suitable **subordinate clause**.

   Will and Mo managed to eat two helpings of cake _____

   _____

3. Tick one box in each row to show whether each sentence contains a **subordinating conjunction** or a **co-ordinating conjunction**.

Sentence	Subordinating conjunction	Co-ordinating conjunction
Mum said I had to tidy my bedroom before I could go outside to play.		
I enjoy playing hockey and tennis.		
We were going to go outside but it started to rain.		
Although it was late, we were allowed to watch the Harry Potter film on TV.		

4. Tick one box in each row to show whether the clauses in bold in each sentence are **main clauses** or **subordinate clauses**.

Sentence	Main clause	Subordinate clause
Our great auntie Dora, **who lives beside the sea**, has invited my sister and me to stay with her.		
After we have been swimming, we always drink hot chocolate.		
Despite being only six, **Karl is much taller than me**.		
Dad chopped the carrots while Mum peeled the potatoes.		

CAN YOU?

- [ ] Say what a noun phrase is.

- [ ] Explain what an expanded noun phrase does.

- [ ] Use a determiner in a noun phrase.

- [ ] Write sentences including expanded noun phrases.

SKILLS CHECK

A noun phrase is a phrase that is about a noun. A noun phrase often includes determiners.

Do you have any apples?

An expanded noun phrase includes more information about the noun.
The noun might be modified by an adjective, another noun and/or a preposition phrase.

Ted was a short man with curly, red hair.

PRACTICE

1. Tick the sentence below that contains an **expanded noun phrase**.

Tick **one**.

After the bell had been rung, we all lined up in the playground. ☐

My dad bakes the most wonderful carrot cake. ☐

Next year, we are going to New Zealand to see our auntie. ☐

My puppy has been chewing slippers and scratching furniture. ☐

2. Underline the **expanded noun phrase** in the sentence below.

Suddenly, an enormous, fire-breathing dragon with flashing red eyes appeared before us!

 **PRACTICE**

3. Underline the longest possible **expanded noun phrase** in each sentence below.

   a. The long, hot summer with barbecues every night was very welcome after the cold winter.

   b. My best friend Lucy in the corner of the room is the girl I was telling you about.

   c. The talented and fantastically brave acrobats were my favourite act.

   d. Mrs Austen, the teacher with the sprained ankle, walks around school on two crutches.

4. Modify the **nouns** on the left to turn them into **expanded noun phrases**.

Noun	Expanded noun phrase
rabbit	
forest	
park	
witch	
fish	

5. Tick the **expanded noun phrases** below that do not contain a **determiner**.

Tick **two**.

several mouldy oranges ☐

a beautiful woman ☐

the happy dogs ☐

deep, blue oceans ☐

my best friend ☐

significant differences ☐

CAN YOU?

☐ Say what a subject is in a sentence.	☐ Say what an object is in a sentence.
☐ Make the verb agree with the subject in the sentence.	☐ Explain the difference between a subject and an object.

SKILLS CHECK

The **subject** in a sentence is the person or thing that is doing or being.

The cat is purring.

The **verb** must agree with the subject in the sentence.

The cat **is** purring.   not   The cat **are** purring.

A verb is a 'doing' or 'being' word.

The cat **is** purring.

The **object** in a sentence is the **noun**, **pronoun** or **noun phrase** that the subject is 'acting upon'.

I stroked **the cat**.

The subject, *I*, is 'acting upon' the object, *the cat*.

 PRACTICE

1. Underline the **subjects** in the sentences below.

   a. The rugby team needs to score a try to qualify for the next round.

   b. The children helped to clear up the mess.

   c. After we had eaten, we relaxed and watched a film.

   d. Joseph was bored and fed up by the end of the summer holiday.

   e. They have a new car that is a very fast automatic and has a soft top.

PRACTICE

2. Which sentence below does not contain an **object**?

Tick **one**.

We have been reading our books all morning. ☐

Those puppies are chewing Mum's new slippers! ☐

I have been tidying and cleaning all morning. ☐

You really love drinking lemonade, don't you? ☐

3. Rewrite the sentences below so that the **verb** agrees with the **subject**.

a. My sister and I am going to the cinema tonight.

_____

b. The school football team are playing at home tomorrow.

_____

4. Underline the **object** in each sentence below.

a. My cat loves to drink milk.

b. Jimmy has sold his old bike.

c. Jack likes to draw and paint pictures.

d. We spent the morning baking cakes and scones.

5. Expand each sentence below by inserting an appropriate **object**.

My mum enjoys cooking.

_____

My brother loves reading.

_____

 **CAN YOU?**

☐ Write using the active and passive voice.

☐ Change a sentence in the active voice into the passive voice, and vice versa.

☐ Say where the subject and object come in active-voice sentences.

☐ Identify which voice is being used in a sentence.

SKILLS CHECK

Writing in the active voice means that the subject of the sentence is doing or being something. If there is an object, it is what the subject is 'acting upon'.

Most writing is in the active voice, but sometimes the passive voice is used, often for a more formal effect.

In passive-voice sentences, the noun, pronoun or noun phrase that would be the object in an active-voice sentence becomes the subject and moves to the start of the sentence.

The subject from the original active-voice sentence moves to the end of the sentence, but it does not become the object. It becomes part of a prepositional phrase and is called the agent. It isn't always included though.

The man was chased.

You form the passive voice by combining the verb **'to be'** with the past participle of whatever verb you are using.

PRACTICE

1. Write a sentence in the **active voice**.

   _____

2. Write a sentence in the **passive voice**.

   _____

3. Tick one box in each row to show whether each sentence is in the **active voice** or **passive voice**.

Sentence	Active voice	Passive voice
I sat by the edge of the lake and watched the ducks.		
Chloe was given a choice of juice or milk.		
Dad carried me to the car when I twisted my ankle.		
The school assembly was led by the Head Teacher.		

4. Rewrite each sentence below in the **passive voice**. Remember to punctuate your sentences correctly.

   a. The twins won the singing competition.

   _____

   b. The fireman rescued the kitten from the top of the tree.

   _____

   c. The bus driver checked our tickets.

   _____

 CAN YOU?

- [ ] Change sentences from the simple present into the simple past.

- [ ] Identify verbs in the present and past progressive.

- [ ] Use a variety of verb tenses in descriptive and other writing.

- [ ] Explain the difference between different types of past tense.

SKILLS CHECK

We use different tenses in our speech and writing to show when and how something happens or happened.

Tense	What it does	Examples
simple present	Tells you about something that is happening now or is often repeated	*I walk to school every Monday.* *We eat breakfast in the mornings at 8 o'clock.*
present progressive	Formed by the present tense of 'to be' + the present participle of the verb	*I am eating my lunch now.* *They are sleeping in the tent.*
simple past	Tells you about something that has happened	*She spoke in assembly yesterday.* *We wrote a story for homework.*
past progressive	Formed by the simple past tense of 'to be' + the present participle of the verb	*Tom was running towards the ice cream van when it drove away.* *They were snoring all night.*
present perfect	Formed by the present tense of 'to have' + the past participle of the verb	*I have written my invitations.* *We have listened to your instructions carefully.*
past perfect	Formed by the past tense of 'to have' + the past participle of the verb	*I had just eaten my breakfast when the doorbell rang.* *After three wonderful days, we had seen all the sights in Rome.*

PRACTICE

1. Rewrite these sentences so that they are in the **simple past tense**.

    a. My sister likes to walk along the coastal path when we are on holiday.

    _____

    b. We eat a piece of toast and drink hot chocolate every night.

    _____

2. Underline the verbs in the **past progressive tense** in this passage.

    Last Sunday, while we were walking along the river path, we saw a mother duck and her six ducklings. They were swimming happily downstream, towards the bridge. Suddenly, a dog started to bark and the ducks turned towards the bank to take cover. We were running over the bridge when we saw them again – they were paddling upstream.

3. Tick the correct box to show the **tense** of the **verb** in each sentence.

Verb	Simple present	Simple past	Present progressive	Past progressive
We were reading *The Jungle Book* today.				
I ate cereal for breakfast.				
They are riding their bikes to school.				
Mum bakes cakes every Saturday morning.				

4. Underline the verb form that is in the **present perfect** in the sentence below.

    We have taken our dog to the vet because he doesn't seem very well.

MODAL VERBS AND ADVERBS

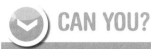

CAN YOU?

- [ ] Give examples of different modal verbs.

- [ ] Estimate the certainty of something expressed by modal verbs.

- [ ] Give examples of different adverbs that express certainty and uncertainty.

- [ ] Choose the correct modal verb or adverb according to context.

SKILLS CHECK

You use modal verbs to change the meaning of the verb that follows. Therefore, modal verbs show:

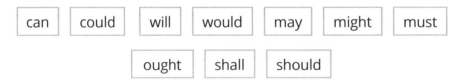

- degrees of **possibility**, for example: It **could** rain today.

- **obligation**, for example: I **ought** to help Mum tidy up.

- **ability**, for example: She **can** speak French and German fluently.

The following are modal verbs:

can	could	will	would	may	might	must

ought	shall	should

Adverbs (for example: *perhaps, surely, definitely, maybe*) can also be used to show how likely – or unlikely – something is.

PRACTICE

1. Underline the **modal verbs** in each of the following sentences.

   a. I might come to Scouts with you tonight.

   b. Mo can abseil down a 20-metre wall.

   c. Dad said I must tidy my room otherwise he won't take me swimming.

   d. You should eat more fruit and vegetables if you want to stay healthy.

PRACTICE

2. Circle the most suitable **modal verb** in each sentence to show certainty.

    a. Mum said she **might / will** take us to the park.

    b. My sister **can / could** play the piano.

    c. We **will / may** take the train to the Lake District in the summer.

3. Which sentences below use a **modal verb** to indicate possibility?

                                                     Tick two.

There could be a storm later tonight. ☐

We can swim five lengths without stopping. ☐

Our old car must be fixed before we can go on holiday. ☐

My sister might wash the dishes. ☐

4. Underline the **adverb** in each sentence that shows certainty or uncertainty.

    a. Mum said perhaps she would invite her friends round for tea.

    b. They will certainly be able to come now that we've changed the date.

    c. Mum clearly hasn't realised what time it is!

    d. She should definitely be more organised next time.

CAN YOU?

- [ ] Use informal speech and language.
- [ ] Tell when non-Standard English is used.
- [ ] Distinguish between formal and informal language.
- [ ] Use the subjunctive mood, where necessary.

SKILLS CHECK

Informal speech and writing is a relaxed and chatty way of communicating that you would normally use with family and friends: "You OK?"

Non-Standard English is also a form of **informal language**, but it is often grammatically incorrect:

I done it already.

For **formal** speech and writing, you use **Standard English**, more formal vocabulary and correct grammar.

I have requested a room with a balcony.   (formal)

I have asked for a room with a balcony.   (informal)

The **subjunctive mood** is used in some very formal speech and writing.

It can also be used to indicate a wish or an imaginary state: If only I **were** a millionaire.

PRACTICE

1. Tick the correct box in each row to indicate whether the writing genre is **formal** or **informal**.

Writing genre	Formal	Informal
your diary		
a letter to your head teacher		
a postcard to your parents		
a text to your best friend		
your speech for a public-speaking competition		

 **PRACTICE**

2. Rewrite each sentence below using **Standard English**.

a. I haven't got none of them.

_____

b. She should of told me she were goin' out.

_____

c. We was hungry coz we didn't have no tea.

_____

d. Me best friend is Fred.

_____

3. Tick the **verb** that would complete the sentence below so that it is in the **subjunctive mood**.

If we _____ to win the lottery, Dad said we would go to the Caribbean for our holidays!

Tick **one**.

should ☐   was ☐   were ☐   are ☐

4. Write a short, chatty, informal postcard to a friend, describing a place you are visiting.

_____   Ciara Matthews
                                            25 Holly Road
_____   Clasterton
                                            CT5 9JU

_____

_____

_____

_____

CAN YOU?

- [ ] Remember to use a capital letter at the start of a sentence.
- [ ] Use capital letters for proper nouns.
- [ ] Choose the correct punctuation mark for different sentences.
- [ ] Use commas correctly in lists and to avoid ambiguity.

SKILLS CHECK

Sentences always start with a capital letter and end with a final punctuation mark.

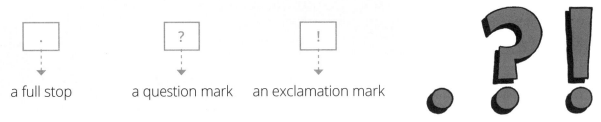

.   a full stop   ?   a question mark   !   an exclamation mark

Capital letters are also used at the start of proper nouns (**Bill**, **Lucy**, **London**) and for the word **I**. Proper nouns name particular people, places (including rivers and mountains), days of the week, months of the year, titles of books and plays… and many more.

Exclamation marks come at the end of an exclamation sentence, but they can also follow an interjection or a command.

        "Ouch!" shouted Zainab.   "Wait for me!"

Commas can be used to separate items in a list and to avoid ambiguity.
In lists, there is no comma before the word *and*.

PRACTICE

1. Which sentence is correctly punctuated?

Tick **one**.

Every Sunday, I go to see my grandmother.	[ ]
My cousin Jamie goes to bank hall school	[ ]
Next week Dad is taking us to see the lion king.	[ ]
Last year, we went on a boat on the river thames.	[ ]

PRACTICE

2. Look at the two sentences below. Explain how using a **comma** changes the meaning.

My favourite pastimes are cooking, my pets and swimming.

My favourite pastimes are cooking my pets and swimming.

_____

_____

3. Complete each sentence by adding a **final punctuation mark** in each box.

a. Our teacher marks our homework every Tuesday ☐

b. What a wonderful surprise it is to see you ☐

c. Please line up and then walk calmly into the assembly ☐

d. What time does your flight leave ☐

4. Rewrite the bullet-pointed list below as a sentence using correct punctuation.

For the science investigation you will need the following:

• a bowl

• a sieve

• rice

• pasta

For the science investigation you will need the following: _____

_____

_____

CAN YOU?

☐ Identify parenthesis in a sentence.

☐ Use brackets, dashes and commas correctly to indicate parenthesis.

☐ Say why parenthesis is used in some sentences.

☐ Remember that the words in parenthesis make no sense on their own.

SKILLS CHECK

Parenthesis means inserting a word or phrase as an explanation or an afterthought into a sentence that would still make sense without it there.

Brackets, dashes and commas can be used to indicate parenthesis and go around the words that sit inside them.

The house, which was white, looked very dirty.

The house – which was white – looked very dirty.

The house (which was white) looked very dirty.

Dashes and commas can only come inside the sentence, whereas brackets can come either inside a sentence or around a whole sentence.

The house was very dirty (even though it was white).

PRACTICE

1. Insert **punctuation** in each of the sentences below to show **parenthesis**.

   a. My best friend Ayesha the one who broke her leg last year has just won a medal in a running race.

   b. After a wonderful meal chicken, roast potatoes, carrots and gravy Mum served the chocolate cake.

   c. The musicians none of whom were over fourteen years old deserved the thunderous applause.

   d. Our dog Rudy not the calmest of canines jumped up and knocked Mum's flowers over.

PRACTICE

2. Punctuate the sentence below to show **parenthesis**.

After a disappointing holiday during which we all got ill we headed to the airport.

3. Write your own sentence containing **parenthesis**. Use **brackets**, **dashes** or **commas** to punctuate it.

_____

_____

4. Tick the sentence below that uses dashes correctly to show **parenthesis**.

Tick **one**.

Prince Harry the brother – of Prince William – raises lots of money for charities. ☐

Prince Harry the brother of Prince William – raises lots of money – for charities. ☐

Prince Harry – the brother of Prince William – raises lots of money for charities. ☐

Prince Harry the brother of Prince William raises – lots of money – for charities. ☐

5. Insert a word, phrase or clause to show **parenthesis** in the gap in each sentence below. Use **brackets**, **dashes** or **commas**.

a. Our teacher _____ is always firm but fair.

b. Today the sun was shining _____ so we went to the park.

SEMI-COLONS, COLONS AND DASHES

CAN YOU?

- ☐ Use colons correctly between two clauses, and also to introduce lists.

- ☐ Use semi-colons instead of full stops to vary sentence length.

- ☐ Use semi-colons to separate items of more than one word in a list.

- ☐ Add dashes to create pauses in writing.

SKILLS CHECK

A colon can be used after a clause and before another clause that explains or gives more detail about the first. It can also introduce a list, a quotation or where a character speaks in a playscript.

It was sunny outside: in fact, it was hot and bright.

In my bag, I have the following: a ruler, a purse and a book.

She said: "It's too hot outside!"

Amanda: It is hot outside.

A semi-colon links two closely related sentences instead of a full stop.
It also separates things in a list where the items are longer than one word.

It was hot; she hid in the shade.

Her bag contained many items: a pretty, pink purse;
a long, blue ruler; and a small book.

Dashes are used to show a break or pause in a sentence, to add suspense or show a change of direction in the sentence.

It was hot – even in the shade.

It was hot – the fire was edging closer.

PRACTICE

1. Match the name of each **punctuation mark** to its symbol.

    a. semi-colon   –

    b. colon   ;

    c. dash   :

PRACTICE

2. Insert a **dash** in the following sentence to show suspense.

    Footsteps approached as we huddled together at the back of the dark, damp cellar; someone was coming to rescue us or were they?

3. Insert **colons** into the following text.

    a. Juliet O Romeo, Romeo, wherefore art thou Romeo?

    b. Romeo [Aside] Shall I hear more, or shall I speak at this?

    c. To make the cake you will need the following butter, eggs, sugar and flour.

    d. We were told to bring waterproof clothes for the trip the weather there is always very unreliable.

4. Rewrite the following sentence so that it contains a **semi-colon**.

    There was so much to do before we left for Scotland we really should have started packing earlier.

    _____

    _____

5. Decide whether a **dash** or **colon** is missing from each sentence below and add it into the correct space.

    a. Once I found the key to the treasure chest, the secret would be revealed assuming it was the right key!

    b. The Evening Herald headline stated No More Tests for Ten-Year-Olds!

    c. This year's school performance was the best one ever my parents had never seen anything like it.

CAN YOU?

☐ Use inverted commas in written speech.

☐ Form the shape of your inverted commas correctly.

☐ Remember that closing inverted commas come after the final punctuation mark.

☐ Write inverted commas at the correct height and in the correct position.

SKILLS CHECK

We use inverted commas – sometimes called **speech marks** – to show where spoken words start and finish. They can also be used for quotations.

"It's a beautiful day," he said.

"To be or not to be."

Opening inverted commas look like back-to-front and upside-down commas. ❝

Closing inverted commas look like normal commas. ❞

Inverted commas can be either **'single'** or **"double"**:

'Hello!'   and   "Goodbye!"

Inverted commas come at the same height as the top of a **capital letter** or **ascender**.

Closing inverted commas must come after the final punctuation mark.

PRACTICE

1. Which sentence below is correctly punctuated?

Tick **one**.

"Where are those cakes I bought at the bakery"? asked Mum, looking puzzled. ☐

"Where are those cakes I bought at the bakery asked Mum?" looking puzzled. ☐

"Where are those cakes I bought at the bakery?" asked Mum, looking puzzled. ☐

"Where are those cakes?" I bought at the bakery asked Mum, looking puzzled. ☐

PRACTICE

2. Insert the missing **inverted commas** in each sentence below.

   a. Dad said, Why don't you go outside to play?

   b. We'd much rather watch television, we replied.

   c. There's a great film on that we've been dying to watch! we added.

   d. Wait until it's raining, then you can watch films, Dad said grumpily.

3. Rewrite the following sentences as **direct speech**. Make sure you add the correct punctuation. Here is an example.

   > The children told their father they would help him tidy up.
   >
   > *"We will help you tidy up," the children told their father.*

   a. The teacher explained that there was a special visitor coming to our assembly.

   _____

   _____

   b. My sister said she would help me with my homework.

   _____

   _____

CAN YOU?

☐ Use apostrophes correctly in contracted words.

☐ Explain what letter (or letters) an apostrophe is replacing.

☐ Write them in the correct position and at the correct height.

☐ Identify where apostrophes might be used incorrectly in words.

SKILLS CHECK

We can use **apostrophes** to show where a letter, or letters, have been left out of words.

| do not | ----▶ | don't |

The **apostrophe** is shaped like a comma but sits at the same height as inverted commas and it must go exactly where the left-out letter (or letters) would be.

| don't |

PRACTICE

1. Write each **contraction** in its full form.

   a. haven't _____

   b. I've _____

   c. didn't _____

   d. they'd _____

   e. shan't _____

PRACTICE

2. Which sentence uses an **apostrophe** for **contraction** correctly?

Tick **one**.

My friends didn't' want to come swimming today. ☐

Wev'e all missed our teacher whos' been off ill. ☐

You should'nt interrupt when someone is talking. ☐

I'd much prefer milk to juice. ☐

3. Write the **contracted form** of each of the following pairs of words.

Word pairs	Contracted form
there is	
shall not	
could have	
it is	
she has	

Word pairs	Contracted form
might not	
you are	
we had	
you have	
I had	

4. The **apostrophes** in six of the **contracted words** in the following passage have been positioned incorrectly. Circle the words and write them correctly on the lines below.

Max was hoping he,d get full marks in his spelling test. He couldn't wait for Friday to come when the'yd all be put to the test. Mrs Smith, his teacher, didn't want it to be too easy for them so she,d promised to include some very challenging words. Max thought he might'nt do as well as he'd hoped when he thought about some of the words he'd come across in his dictionary. Just then, the head teacher came in. She'd come to tell them that Mrs Smith woul'dnt be in as she'd caught a cold! "Its' just not fair!" thought Max.

_____   _____

_____   _____

_____   _____

APOSTROPHES FOR POSSESSION

CAN YOU?

- ☐ Use a possessive apostrophe correctly.
- ☐ Tell whom an object belongs to from the word that has an apostrophe.
- ☐ Add an extra 's' followed by an apostrophe to proper nouns ending in 's'.
- ☐ Rephrase sentences to show possession, using an apostrophe.

SKILLS CHECK

Apostrophes can show that something belongs to someone. They are the same shape as a comma and you put them at the same height as inverted commas.

John's cat is black.

If you use an apostrophe to show possession, you put it after the final letter of the noun, and then add an 's' in singular nouns and in irregular plurals.

The house's door is red.   **The children's class is small.**   (irregular plural)

In plural nouns ending in 's' you add the apostrophe after the 's'.

The houses' doors are red.

For proper nouns ending in 's', an apostrophe comes after the final 's' and is followed by an extra 's'.

Charles's banana was yellow.

PRACTICE

1. Why has an **apostrophe** been used in the sentence below?

   The children's dog jumped in the pond.

   Tick **one.**

   to show that the dog belongs to the children ☐

   to show that the children belong to the dog ☐

   to show a contraction ☐

   to show that children is in the plural ☐

PRACTICE

2. Rewrite the following phrases using an **apostrophe** to indicate **possession**.
The first one has been done for you.

Phrase	Phrase with apostrophe
the schoolbag belonging to Sam	Sam's schoolbag
the purse belonging to Mum	
the poem belonging to James	
the books belonging to the children	
the anniversary of our parents	

3. Which sentence below has been punctuated correctly with an **apostrophe**?

Tick **one**.

Some princesses' crowns are made with diamonds and pearls. ☐

Some princesse's crowns are made with diamonds and pearls. ☐

Some princes'ss crowns are made with diamonds and pearls. ☐

Some princess' crowns are made with diamonds and pearls. ☐

4. Rewrite the sentences below, inserting the missing **apostrophe** in each.

a. Johns milk was very cold.

_____

b. The womens scarves were brightly coloured.

_____

CAN YOU?

☐ Break up large amounts of text using bullet points.

☐ Use three dots (...) to signify an ellipsis.

☐ Remember that colons often come before bullet points.

☐ Use ellipses to indicate interruption, suspense or omission.

SKILLS CHECK

Bullet points:

- are used to list information vertically
- often come after a sentence ending with a colon
- are used to draw the reader's attention to important information

The text following each bullet point does not need to start with a capital letter or end with a full stop if it is not a full sentence.

Ellipses – three dots (...) – can be used to show that words or sentences have been intentionally left out of a text. This can be to show suspense, a pause or interruption, or to indicate that unnecessary words have been removed from a longer text.

PRACTICE

1. Which of these punctuation marks can be used to show a pause or an interruption?

Tick **two.**

full stop ☐

dash ☐

exclamation mark ☐

ellipses ☐

semi-colon ☐

PRACTICE

2. Rewrite each of the following sentences, inserting an **ellipsis** to show suspense or tension.

   a. We knew we were about to be rescued from the dark forest or were we?

   _____

   b. At the end of the tunnel, we could see a shaft of light this could be our one last hope.

   _____

3. Rewrite this sentence as a list using **bullet points**.

   To make fresh fruit salad, you will need the following: apples, oranges, pears, pineapples and a large bowl.

   _____

   _____

   _____

   _____

   _____

4. A mistake has been made in the punctuation of this list. Circle the mistake.

   If you are planning a holiday in the south of France, you might like to visit;

   - the beautiful, sandy beaches;
   - the delightful, historic villages;
   - the towering churches.

CAN YOU?

☐ Explain what ambiguity means.

☐ Use hyphens correctly in compound words.

☐ Describe what a compound word is.

☐ Explain the difference between hyphenated and non-hyphenated words.

SKILLS CHECK

We use the word **ambiguity** to describe when a word or a group of words can have more than one meaning, especially if we do not punctuate it correctly. To avoid ambiguity, we can use hyphens:

- in **compound words** (two describing words that come before a noun)

a heavy-metal detector   (not a heavy metal detector)

- to make a distinction between two words whose meaning could be ambiguous without it

re-sign = to sign again   resign = to quit

- to join **prefixes** to some **root words**, especially if they begin with a vowel

order → re-order   operate → co-operate

PRACTICE

1. Insert a **hyphen** into each sentence so that it contains a **compound word**.

   a. My big sister only drinks sugar free tea and coffee.

   b. When we went to Australia on holiday, we saw a man eating shark.

   c. I read a book about time travelling cats.

   d. Dad is a hard working man who never sits down.

2. Show that you know the difference in meaning between the following words by writing a sentence using each one in context.

   a. re-form _____

   b. reform _____

   c. re-cover _____

   d. recover _____

CAN YOU?

- [ ] Tell the difference between a synonym and an antonym.
- [ ] List words that are antonyms of each other.
- [ ] Think of different synonyms for a given word.
- [ ] Make a word negative by adding a prefix to it.

SKILLS CHECK

We use the word **synonym** to describe words that have the same, or very similar, meanings.

| cry | ←--→ | sob | ←--→ | weep |

Care is needed when choosing a synonym as the meaning might not fit the context of the sentence.

Antonyms are words that are opposite in meaning.

Many antonyms are made by adding a negative prefix to the root word.

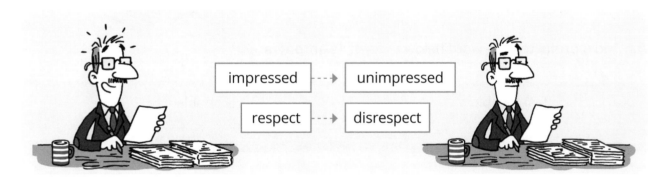

impressed ---→ unimpressed

respect ---→ disrespect

PRACTICE

1. Which word is closest in meaning to <u>hinder</u>?

Tick **one**.

a. to fall over ☐

b. to get in the way ☐

c. to annoy ☐

d. to throw away ☐

PRACTICE

2. Which two words in the sentence below are **synonyms** of each other?

We made sure that the soil that the seeds were in was damp. Our teacher said if it wasn't moist, they would have less chance of growing strong and healthy.

_____ and _____

3. Which word is similar in meaning to <u>weary</u>?

Tick **one**.

a. exhausted ☐

b. tearful ☐

c. weak ☐

d. confused ☐

4. Add a **prefix** to each word below to form its **antonym**.

a. _____fashionable

d. _____probable

b. _____legal

e. _____regular

c. _____continue

f. _____likely

5. Draw a line to match each word to its **antonym**.

spacious	cheerful
distraught	beneficial
useless	cowardly
fearless	small

CAN YOU?

☐ Say what roots and word families are.

☐ Identify words that come from the same root.

☐ Use knowledge of root words to work out the meaning of new words.

☐ Say what a common prefix in a word family means.

SKILLS CHECK

Words with the same root can be grouped into word families. This can help you work out the meaning of new words and aid your spelling.

For example, the root 'medic' is used in the word family *medicine, medical, medication, medicinal* and the root 'circ' is used in the word family *circle, circumference, circus*.

Sometimes, a silent letter is sounded when the root is in a different word:

| sounded 'g' | si**g**nature | silent 'g' | si**g**n |

Sometimes, an **unstressed vowel** is **stressed** when the root is in a different word.

| unstressed | de**fin**ite | stressed | **fin**ite |

PRACTICE

1. What is the meaning of the root '**graph**' in the word family below?

> telegraph   grapheme   autograph   biography

Tick **one**.

a. send ☐   b. draw ☐

c. write ☐   d. speak ☐

2. Circle the word that does not belong to the **word family** below.

> definite   define   infinity   financial   indefinitely

 PRACTICE

3. Add a prefix to the root 'ceive' to make a verb.

_____

4. What does the root 'vis' mean in each word below?

| television   visual   visibility   invisible |

Tick **one**.

a. disappear ☐

b. see ☐

c. distant ☐

d. faint ☐

5. How many words can you make using the prefix 'super'? Write your words around the edge of the oval.

SUPER

What does the root 'super' mean? _____

_____

CAN YOU?

☐ Change verbs into adjectives and adverbs by adding suffixes.

☐ Change verbs into adjectives and nouns by adding suffixes.

☐ Add suffixes starting with a vowel to words ending in 'fer'.

☐ Say what a root word is.

SKILLS CHECK

Some **verbs** can be changed to **adjectives** and **adverbs** by adding the suffixes '**able**' and '**ably**' and '**ible**' and '**ibly**'.

understand ---→ understandably   digest ---→ digestible

The suffixes '**able**' and '**ably**' are much more common than the suffixes '**ible**' and '**ibly**'.

Some **verbs** can be changed to **adjectives** and **nouns** by adding the endings '**ant**', '**ance**', '**ancy**', '**ent**', '**ence**' and '**ency**'.

inform ---→ informant   insist ---→ insistent

When you add a suffix beginning with a vowel to words ending in '**fer**', you double the '**r**' if '**fer**' is still stressed when the suffix is added. If '**fer**' is not stressed, you do not double the '**r**'.

infer ---→ inferred   refer ---→ reference

PRACTICE

1. Change these verbs to adjectives and adverbs by adding the **suffixes** 'able', 'ible', 'ably' or 'ibly'.

Verb	Adjective	Adverb
advise		
flex		
force		
comfort		

PRACTICE

2. Change these **verbs** to **adjectives** and **nouns** by adding the **suffixes** 'ant', 'ance', 'ancy', 'ent', 'ence' or 'ency'. You will need to change the spelling of the root for one of them.

Verb	Adjective	Noun
relate		
obey		
vacate		
persist		

3. Add 'ed', 'ence' and 'ing' to the following **verbs**, remembering the spelling rule.

	ed	ence	ing
differ			
refer			
prefer			

4. Name a **suffix** that can be used to change a **noun** into an **adverb**, and give an example.

_____

5. Name a **suffix** that can be used to change a **verb** into a **noun**, and give an example.

_____

CAN YOU?

☐ Add a suffix to a noun to make an adjective.

☐ Work out how an adjective is spelled by using certain rules.

SKILLS CHECK

To turn **nouns** into **adjectives**, we can add **suffixes**. For example:

Suffix	Noun	Adjective	Rule
'cious' (pronounced /**shus**/)	*space*	*spacious*	If the root word ends in '**ce**', the /**sh**/ sound is usually spelt as '**c**'.
'tious' (pronounced /**shus**/)	*caution*	*cautious*	If the noun ends in '**tion**', the adjective usually takes the suffix '**tious**'.
'cial' (pronounced /**shul**/)	*office*	*official*	'**cial**' is common after a vowel.
'tial' (pronounced /**shul**/)	*essence*	*essential*	'**tial**' usually comes after a consonant.

PRACTICE

1. Turn the following **nouns** into **adjectives** by using the **suffixes** 'cious' or 'tious'.

a. grace _____

b. nutrition _____

c. malice _____

d. infection _____

e. ambition _____

PRACTICE

2. Turn the following **nouns** into **adjectives** by using the **suffixes** 'cial' or 'tial'.

   a. space _____

   b. resident _____

   c. office _____

   d. president _____

   e. face _____

3. The following words have been spelled as they sound. Write the correct spelling for each.

Incorrect spelling	Correct spelling
speshul	
pretenshus	
crushul	
vishus	
inishul	
suspishus	

CAN YOU?

☐ Say where you add a prefix to a word.   ☐ Indentify prefixes with a negative meaning.

SKILLS CHECK

A **root** is a word or part of a word to which **prefixes** can be added to make new words from the same **word family**. You add most **prefixes** to the start of the root without changing the spelling.

| appear | ---→ | disappear |

The prefixes '**un**', '**dis**', '**mis**', '**il**', '**ir**' and '**in**' have a negative meaning (though '**in**' can also mean *in/into*).

regular – irregular   *kind – unkind*

The prefix '**re**' usually means to repeat or to do again.

reappear

Some prefixes come from Greek and Latin. Knowing the meaning of these will help you to know the meaning of some words and how to spell them in English.

 PRACTICE

1. Add the **prefix** 're' to each of the words below and then write a short sentence containing each new word. One has been done for you.

cycle	recycle	We recycle our glass and plastic.
appear		
cover		
construct		

PRACTICE

2. Match each **prefix** to a **suffix** to form a complete word.

geo		sect
hemi		graphy
bi		graph
auto		sphere

3. Add the **prefix** 'uni' to the following **root words**. Write the new words on the lines.

cycle _____

form _____

The prefix 'uni' means _____

4. Add the **prefix** 'tele' to the following **root words**. Write the new words on the lines.

scope _____

vision _____

The prefix 'tele' means _____

5. Add the **prefix** 'sub' to the following **root words**. Write the new words on the lines.

marine _____

way _____

The prefix 'sub' means _____

 **CAN YOU?**

- [ ] Explain what a homophone is.
- [ ] Give examples of homophones.

- [ ] Describe what a near-homophone is.
- [ ] Give examples of near-homophones.

SKILLS CHECK

Homophones are words that sound the same but have a different meaning and spelling.

tale   *tail*

Some words sound almost the same but have a different meaning and spelling.
These words are called near-homophones.

accept   *except*

PRACTICE

1. Circle the correct **homophone** in the following sentences.

   a. I don't know what the **weather / whether** will be like tomorrow.

   b. You need lots of **flower / flour** to make bread.

   c. He wasn't **allowed / aloud** to go to the cinema.

   d. "Stop being so **vain / vane**!"

PRACTICE

2. Write a matching **homophone** for each word. There might be more than one.

Word	Homophone	Word	Homophone
whale		stare	
root		isle	
pour		dew	
alter		main	
guessed		toe	
heard		road	
precede		towed	
affect		scene	
bawl		so	

 CAN YOU?

- [ ] Say what a silent letter is.
- [ ] Spell words with silent letters correctly.
- [ ] Give examples of words that have silent letters.

SKILLS CHECK

There are many different words which contain silent letters.

Silent letter	Examples
'k' is always at the beginning of a word and is followed by an 'n'	*know*
'g' is followed by an 'n'	*gnat*
'h' goes with other letters, especially 'w' and 'r'	*where*
'b' is almost always at the end of a word preceded by the letter 'm'	*tomb*
'l' (in the same syllable) comes between: 'a' and 'k' 'a' and 'f ' 'a' and 'v' 'a' and 'm' 'o' and 'k' before 'd'	*walk* *calf* *halve* *calm* *yolk* *would*
'd' comes before a consonant	*edge*
'n' usually follows an 'm'	*hymn*
's' comes before an 'l'	*aisle*
'p' is usually at the beginning of a word, often of Greek or Latin origin	*pneumonia*
't' comes after an 's'	*whistle*
'c' comes after an 's'	*muscle*

 **PRACTICE**

1. Complete the following words by writing in the missing **silent letters**.

   ___nuckle   ___night   ___nome   w___ite   r___ombus

2. In the sentences below, two words are spelt incorrectly. Write the correct spellings underneath.

   a. Last autum, we went to an iland just off the coast of Scotland.

   _____ and _____

   b. Mum made me a lovely sandwich wich she cut in haf.

   _____ and _____

3. Complete the words in each sentence by adding the missing letters.

   a. A serious illness of the lungs is called ___n___ ___mon___a.

   b. Our dog comes back to us when he hears his w___is___l___.

   c. The climbers' as___e___ ___ of Mount Everest was a great victory.

4. Unscramble these anagrams to make words containing silent letters.

   a. flac _____

   b. bilmc _____

   c. gede _____

   d. lsiae _____

CAN YOU?

☐ Give examples of **'ough'** words that have the **/oa/** sound.

☐ Think of other sounds the letter-string **'ough'** makes.

☐ Spell words containing **'ough'** correctly.

SKILLS CHECK

The letter-string 'ough' can be used for a number of different sounds. Read the following words aloud to hear the difference.

> enough   through   dough   bought

PRACTICE

1. Write the words below in the correct column according to the sound that their **'ough'** letter string makes. The **'ough'** letters should make the same sound as the word at the top.

> enough   although   bough   tough   thought   dough   plough
> ought   trough   bought   borough   fought   brought

thorough	rough	slough

sought	though	cough

CAN YOU?

☐ Remember the **'ei'** after **'c'** spelling rule.

☐ List exceptions to the **'ie'** rule.

☐ Give examples of words with a long **/ee/** sound spelled **'ie'**.

☐ Memorise exception words that have no spelling rule.

SKILLS CHECK

Normally, words that have a long /ee/ sound are spelled 'ie'.

| field | yield | wield |

There are exceptions to this rule though.

| protein | seize | neither | either | caffeine |

When the /ee/ sound comes after the letter 'c', it is usually spelled 'ei':

| ceiling | receive | deceive |

The letters 'ei' also have other sounds, such as /ay/.

| neighbours | weight | freight |

Any other exceptions are words that need learning as there is no rule.

| science | glacier | ancient |

PRACTICE

1. Group the words below according to the spelling rule.

ceiling   conceited   caffeine   receipt   field   deceit   yield   shriek

grief   achieve   piece   weird   seize   siege   thief   brief   niece

shield   protein   receive   fierce   belief

Words with an 'ie' spelling and an /ee/ sound	Words with an 'ei' spelling and an /ee/ sound following a 'c'	Exceptions

 CAN YOU?

Understand the test paper.

SKILLS CHECK

The Grammar, Punctuation and Spelling test has two parts:

A short-answer grammar, punctuation and vocabulary test
A spelling test

The Grammar, Punctuation and Vocabulary test is timed. You need to answer as many of the questions as possible – make sure you don't run out of time.

For the spelling test, you won't be strictly timed, but you'll have to listen out for the spellings. Make sure you don't miss any. It's important that you write your answers in the correct sentence.

Read the questions carefully. Then read them again.
Make sure you understand what the question is asking you to do.

If you're struggling with a question, move on and return to it at the end.

If you have time to spare and have a few questions unanswered, just have a go – you don't lose marks for trying.

Write as clearly as you can.

Try to spend the last five minutes checking your work.

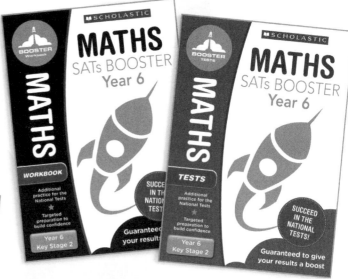

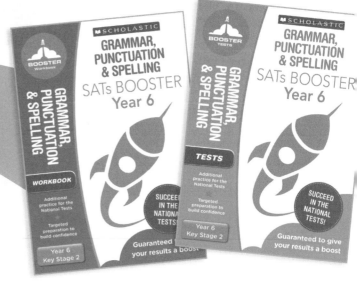
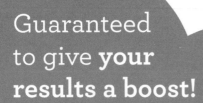